HAYDN

Selected Keyboard Sonatas

BOOK II

Edited and annotated by

HOWARD FERGUSON

THE ASSOCIATED BOARD OF
THE ROYAL SCHOOLS OF MUSIC

THEMATIC INDEX

The small bracketed numerals give the numbering of the Keyboard Sonatas in Anthony van Hoboken's *Joseph Haydn: Thematisch-bibliographisches Werkverzeichnis*; Schott, Mainz 1957

INTRODUCTION

Franz Joseph Haydn was born of humble parents in Rohrau, Lower Austria, on 31 March 1732. At the age of eight he became a choirboy in St Stephen's Cathedral, Vienna. In his mid-teens, when his voice had broken, he had to leave the choir and times were often hard. But in 1761 he entered the service of the princely house of Esterházy, was made Kapellmeister five years later, and remained in the post for the rest of his life. He paid two highly successful visits to England in 1791–2 and 1794–5, and died in Vienna at the height of his fame on 31 May 1809. His enormous output, which included 68 String Quartets and over 100 Symphonies, contributed largely to the development of the Classical Style and was crowned by the great Oratorios and Masses of his later years.

Many of Haydn's keyboard Sonatas circulated widely during his lifetime, but because of hazards of source transmission their total number has never been agreed. It seemed possible that the problem might have been solved when Anthony van Hoboken published the first volume of his monumental catalogue, *Joseph Haydn: Thematisch-bibliographisches Werkverzeichnis*; Schott, Mainz 1957. But the hope was vain. Previously unknown works have since been discovered and others found to be spurious, with the result that the present count varies between 60 and 62 Sonatas. The two most recent editions that aim at completeness are edited by respectively Christa Landon (Wiener Urtext Edition, Vienna & London 1964–6, with an important separate Textual Commentary: *Kritische Anmerkungen*; Urtext Edition 1982, in German only); and Georg Feder (Henle Verlag, München-Duisberg 1972). Both refer to the generally accepted Hoboken numbering of the Sonatas; but it is typical of the general muddle of Haydn publication that their own numberings are entirely different.

The aim of the present selection of 23 Sonatas is to provide an introduction to these lovely and still too-little-known works. They range in difficulty from the simplest in Book I to the fairly advanced in Book IV. The more demanding of the late Sonatas, such as the magnificent E flat, Hob.XVI/52, have not been included.

SOURCES

Only thirteen of the Sonatas have survived in Haydn's autograph, and not all of these are complete. The rest are known either from early editions or from contemporary copyists' manuscripts, the most important of which are listed in the *Kritische Anmerkungen* to the Wiener Urtext Edition, mentioned above.

The early works were named by Haydn either *Partitta* (see the facsimile of Sonata in G, Hob.XVI/6, frontispiece to Book I), or *Divertimento*. The earliest surviving autograph to bear the title *Sonata* is that of the Sonata in C minor, Hob.XVI/20, dated 1771 but not included in the present selection.

THE INSTRUMENTS

During the period in which the works were written, the harpsichord and clavichord were being gradually superseded by the fortepiano, the forerunner of the modern piano. The early instruments differed from one another tonally in three main respects: 1) the harpsichord was unable to produce the continuously graded dynamics natural to both clavichord and fortepiano; 2) neither harpsichord nor fortepiano could produce the expressive *Bebung* (vibrato) of the clavichord; 3) the clavichord's tone, though capable of subtle variation, was so delicate that the instrument's usefulness was restricted to the home.

The early Sonatas are always described in the sources as being 'per il clavicembalo' (for the harpsichord); and their total lack of dynamic markings suggest that that was indeed the instrument for which they were intended. The Sonata in C minor, already mentioned, is curiously anomalous however, for although it is described on the autograph as being 'per il Clavi Cembalo', it contains dynamic markings that were quite impractical on the harpsichord. Moreover, when it was first published (Artaria, Vienna 1780) it was described as being 'per il clavicembalo o forte piano' (for harpsichord or fortepiano), as was then becoming customary. So far as is known from existing autographs, Haydn himself did not specify the fortepiano until the Sonata in E flat, Hob.XVI/49, which is dated 1790.

DYNAMICS

Contemporary title-pages, such as that of the above-mentioned Sonata in C minor, confirm what we might already suspect: namely, that during this period of transition players would have used whatever type of instrument happened to be available. Moreover, there can be little doubt that if Haydn had been playing one of his own early, unmarked Sonatas on the fortepiano, he would have made full use of the instrument's expressive dynamic capabilities. On a modern piano we should do likewise, while remembering always that textures should be kept transparent and dynamics moderate, as they would have been on any of the earlier instruments.

As a guide to users of the present edition, suggested editorial dynamics have been added within square brackets to those works that have few or none. It must be understood, however, that they have no textual authority; and that they leave the player to provide all those small local inflections – *crescendos, diminuendos*, etc. – that instinct tells him the music requires.

TEMPO

Haydn's tempo marks – like those of C.P.E. Bach whom he greatly admired – may at times suggest to the player of today a quicker speed than the music requires. This is specially true of duple-time Allegros – particularly if they contain semiquaver triplets or sextuplets – as such movements nearly always require the quaver to be brisk rather than the crotchet. It is wise, therefore, before tackling any movement to look ahead and see what is the smallest note-value used: for that will generally provide a clue to the correct tempo. In the present edition a suggested editorial metronome mark has been added within square brackets at the end of every movement; but like the editorial dynamics, it is neither authoritative nor binding.

STACCATO DOTS (·) & WEDGES (ˈ)

Haydn used the wedge sign (ˈ) or dash (ˈ) to indicate a normal staccato, not a staccatissimo as was later customary. He used dots, either slurred (♩̣ ♩̣ ♩̣) or unslurred (♩̣ ♩̣ ♩̣), for mezzo-staccato, particularly in groups of repeated notes. Though the distinction was not always preserved by contemporary copyists and engravers, it has been thought best in the present edition to reproduce whichever sign appears in the source concerned.

ORNAMENTATION

Haydn's admiration of C.P.E. Bach suggests that he would have accepted the interpretation of ornaments given in Bach's treatise, *Versuch über die wahre Art das Clavier zu spielen*, Part I, 1753; Part II, 1762; enlarged 3rd edition, 1778 (English translation by William J. Mitchell, *Essay on the true art of playing keyboard instruments*; New York & London 1949, reprinted Eulenburg Books, London 1974: see Part I, Chapter 2, Embellishments). Peculiar to Haydn, however, is the so-called Haydn Ornament (~), whose interpretation is discussed below.

The ornaments found in the present volumes are listed below, together with their interpretations. All of them, with the exception of the Turn (∾) when it occurs between two notes, begin *on* the beat and are diatonic within the key that prevails at the moment, unless the contrary is shown by a small accidental above or below the sign.

Shake (*Triller*): ∿, ∿∿, *t*, *tr*, ∿, ∿.

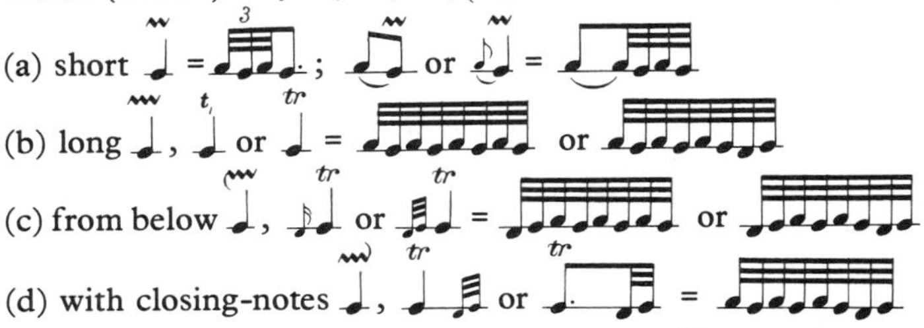

(a) short

(b) long

(c) from below

(d) with closing-notes

In a quick tempo (a) may be played thus:

(i.e.): or ; or, by analogy with Bach's very short mordent (see below):

More often than in the 17th century, *tr* indicates a long shake and ∿ a short one; but the distinction is not always observed. In the second realization of both (b) and (c) the last two notes, the so-called closing-notes (*Nachschlag*), may be added at the discretion of the player to improve the shape or flow of a passage, particularly at the end of a long shake, and at the end of a short shake when the following note is one degree higher. Long shakes (with or without closing-notes) usually last for the whole of the written value of the note; but without closing-notes they sometimes end earlier.

A shake starts with the auxiliary, except:

1) when it is preceded by and slurred to the note one degree above the main note, as in the second realization of (a);

2) probably also (though there is no documentary proof of this) when it is preceded by a long appoggiatura one degree above the main note, even if unslurred, since a slur is always implied between a long appoggiatura and its resolution (see *Single small note*, below);

3) when it is preceded by a small note one degree below the main note, or by a three-note slide of small notes (upward or downward) whose middle note is the same as the main note.

Turn (*Doppelschlag*): ∾

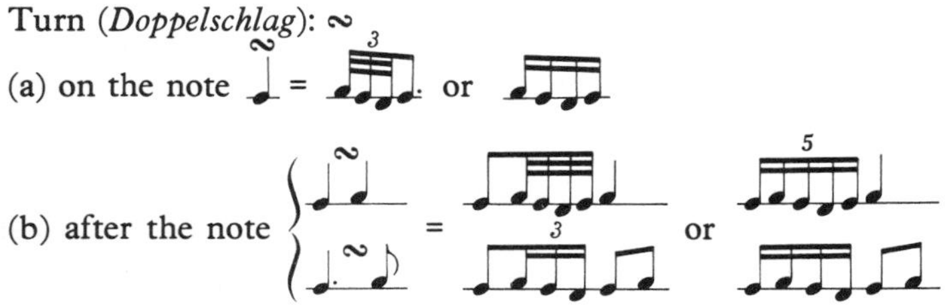

(a) on the note or

(b) after the note = or

or some rhythmic variant of these notes.

The Haydn Ornament: ~.

Haydn often used this sign to stand for a Turn on the note, thus: or . The interpretation is proved by one of his pieces for musical clock, of which the autograph gives the rhythm , while the clock (which still survives) plays . (The sign should not be mistaken for the later Inverted Turn: , which Haydn always wrote in small or normal-sized notes: or .)

Mordent (*Mordent*): ∿.

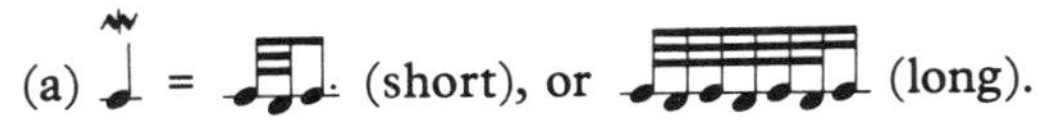

(a) (short), or (long).

When a mordent occurs on a very short note, Bach suggests striking the main note and the auxiliary simultaneously, then releasing the latter, thus: .

Single small note (*Vorschlag, Appoggiatura*):

An appoggiatura is played on the beat and subtracts its value (not necessarily the one shown) from that of the following normal-sized note. There are two main types:

(a) the long, which takes the accent, is slurred to the main note and is usually, but not invariably, half the value of the latter (a third or two-thirds as long when the main note is dotted);

(b) the short, which is unaccented and quick.

Since the two types are seldom differentiated graphically, the player must decide which one is intended in each instance. In this connection it is helpful to remember that one of the main functions of a long appoggiatura is to supply an expressive accent: hence, if the main note is already accented in some way, the appoggiatura will tend to be short. This is most likely to occur in the following instances:

1) if the main note itself is short or staccato;
2) if the main note is syncopated;
3) if the main note is part of a triplet;
4) if the main note rises a 2nd, then falls;
5) if the main note is repeated several times;
6) if the main note is more discordant than the small one.

In the present edition all short appoggiaturas are indicated by a small ♪ printed above or below the stave; the rest are long.

Group of small notes: , , , etc.

Groups of small notes generally begin on the beat and take their value (not necessarily the one shown) from the following normal-sized note.

or (= ∾ & the Haydn Ornament ~)

or

or (= an Inverted Turn)

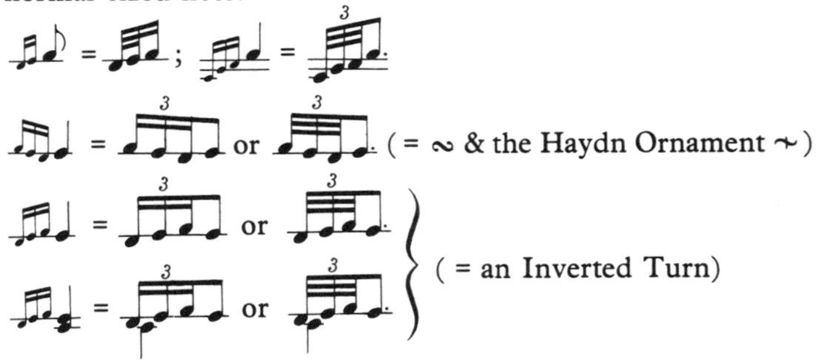

Arpeggio:

The sign shows that the chord should be broken upwards, generally beginning on the beat, either quickly or slowly as the context suggests. (In some Haydn sources the arpeggio is indicated by an oblique line drawn through the chord, but the sign is not reproduced in modern editions.)

THIS EDITION

The Editorial Notes list the source(s) used for each Sonata; otherwise they are devoted mainly to questions of performance and study. In the music pages, numbered footnotes deal with textual matters and lettered footnotes with points of interpretation. A realization of each ornament is shown above or below the stave at its first appearance in every piece. *All* short appoggiaturas are indicated by a small 𝅘𝅥𝅮 similarly placed. Redundant accidentals have been omitted. Editorial accidentals, notes, rests, dynamics, etc., are printed either in small type or within square brackets, and editorial slurs and ties are crossed with a small vertical stroke. Curved brackets indicate that a note should not be struck. Generally r.h. notes have been placed on the upper stave and l.h. notes on the lower; but occasionally it has been more convenient to use the signs ⌊ and ⌈ to indicate the r.h. and l.h. respectively.

Warmest thanks are due to the following for providing photocopies of sources or allowing access to 1st editions, and for giving permission for the material to be used in establishing the present texts: Staatsbibliothek Preussischer Kulturbesitz, Musikabteilung, Berlin; Deutsche Staatsbibliothek, Berlin/DDR; Wissenschaftliche Allgemeinbibliothek, Schwerin; Österreichische Nationalbibliothek, Musik-Sammlung, Vienna; Gesellschaft der Musikfreunde, Vienna; Niederösterreichische Landesarchiv, Vienna; Bibliothèque Nationale, Paris; The British Library Board, London; Royal College of Music, London; Dr Alan Tyson, London; Cambridge University Library; and The Provost & Fellows of King's College, Cambridge.

HOWARD FERGUSON
Cambridge 1983

EDITORIAL NOTES

1 SONATA in D, Hob.XVI/14

Sources used:

A No.5 of an early copyist's MS titled *V Divertimenti per il Clavicembalo del sig.r Giuseppe Hayden.* (Dr Alan Tyson, London.)

B 1st edition: No.4 of *Five easy and familiar sonatas for the harpsichord or pianoforte with an accompaniment for the violin, and a duett, for two performers on one instrument composed by Pleyel*; J.Cooper, London [c.1790].

In B the attribution to Pleyel appears to refer to the keyboard 'duett', and possibly also to the Sonata in A, Hob.XVI/5 (not included in the present volumes), since the remaining four Sonatas appear in A, though in slightly variant versions and without violin 'accompaniment'.

The Menuet (without a Trio) reappears in a copyist's MS as No.18 of *[18] Menuetti per il Cembalo. Dal Sig.re Giuseppe Hayden*, Hob.IX/20.

The present text follows A, and also refers to B.

I Allegro moderato

As in many of the *Allegro* movements in Book I, demisemiquavers and semiquaver sextuplets here show that the quick beat applies to quavers rather than crotchets. The general mood is of a comfortably relaxed *cantabile*.

The shake in r.h. b.3 is best interpreted as shown above the stave, i.e. without a *Nachschlag*, since tied-A G F(sharp) G would anticipate the *appoggiatura* in the following bar. In b.17 a new phrase begins on beat 1. Separate it fractionally from the previous bar by giving the latter its implied *dim.*, and very slightly accenting the F(sharp) on beat 1. The syncopations in r.h. bb.21–23 should be underlined thus [music example], with a *legato* l.h. In bb.28–30, beginning with the 2nd quaver, *molto legato* provides a contrast to the detached semiquaver triplets in r.h. bb.32–33.

Though the development passage beginning at b.49 is made up of a 4-step descending sequence of paired bars, it is best treated as a single long line that finally blossoms into the *cresc.* of b.56. Similarly, the unchanging figuration of bb.65–70 also suggests a single line, though in fact it consists of 2 + 4 bars.

II Menuet

Slightly different realizations have been suggested for the shakes in b.4, etc., and b.24, etc., in keeping with the contrasted characters of the Menuet and the Trio. The former is forthright and vigorous and the latter more gentle and lyrical.

III Presto

The quizzical mood of the movement is immediately apparent from the abrupt 2-bar 'question' at the very opening, with its totally unexpected interrupted cadence. (In b.4 the shake is probably best interpreted as shown, for there would scarcely be sufficient time for a sextuplet.) Equally abrupt is the 3-bar answer to the 'question' (bb.3–5). After both have been repeated the music broadens into extended semiquaver movement, in which, following initial 2- and 4-bar phrases, a fresh surprise is afforded by nine bars (not eight) closing on the dominant of A (bb.23–31). Here the 'question' is repeated three times – the suggested dynamics are equally quirky – the eventual answer being decisively confirmed by the final 4 bars of the exposition.

At the end of the development the recapitulation slips in unobtrusively (b.72) with the equivalent of b.11 rather than b.1, thus avoiding too many repetitions of the 'question'. Moreover, the feeling of development continues for a further eight bars, leaving the music poised on the dominant of D, for the return of the 2nd-subject group at b.80. Having thus achieved its tonal goal, the rest of the recapitulation proceeds on its way unchanged.

2 SONATA in G, Hob.XVI/27

Sources used:

A An early copyist's MS titled *In G♯* [i.e. G major] *Sonata per il Clavicembalo Del Sig.re Giuseppe Haydn.* (Schwerin, Wissenschaftliche Allgemeinbibliothek, Sign.Mus.2631.)

B 1st edition: No.1 of *Six Sonates Pour le Clavecin ou le Piano Forte . . . Oeuvre XIV*; J.J.Hummel, Berlin & Amsterdam [1778], Pl.No.390.

C *Oeuvres complettes*, Cahier XI/1; Breitkopf & Härtel, Leipzig 1799–1806.

The present text follows A, and also refers to B & C.

I Allegro con brio

A clue to the correct tempo is provided by the r.h. ornamentation in b.1. Though the whole movement is lively (*con brio*), the crotchet beat should not be so quick as to turn b.1 into a scramble, or hide the fact that the ornament-notes are slightly less important than the rhythm  . In bb.2 & 4 the last three quavers in each hand should be lightly detached; likewise the final l.h. quaver in b.5. Apart from that, bb.1–8 are *legato cantabile*, with the smallest of breaks in b.6 between r.h. notes 1 & 2. Mark clearly the 2-note slurs in bb.36–37, so that they contrast with the *staccatos* in the *p* repetition of the phrase in the following bars.

In the development the listener must be made aware of the underlying structure, which is as follows. Bb.58–73 consist of two 8-bar sentences, with harmonic climaxes at respectively bb.63 & 71, and resolutions at b.65 (E minor) and b.73. One expects the latter to be on the chord of B major, but an A-natural in the l.h. turns it into a dominant 7th, which prompts a 2-bar descending figure to enter in the r.h. on the 2nd quaver. The bass mounts through similar 7ths on E & A, and appears about to complete the sequence on D, when instead it moves to an inverted 7th chord on C (b.76). As it does so there is a melodic overlap in the r.h., where notes 3–4 of the descending figure also serve as notes 1–2 of a new 2-bar phrase. This is echoed (*p*), then developed in a *cresc.* that ends the development on a pause seven bars later. (A *rit.* is needed in b.85.)

II Menuet

Phrase the Menuet thus:

b.1 *b.9*

But note that in bb.19–22 the 1-bar phrases begin with an upbeat crotchet or quaver-triplet. The quaint repetitions of b.29 at different octaves suggest a *dim.* leading to *p* on the twin pauses in b.32.

In the Trio a clear break is needed between notes 1 & 2 of b.44, etc.:  . In bb.56–57 the gracenotes should be short, because the accent must fall on the first note of each pair of 'sighing' quavers. It seems likely that the ornaments in b.65 (𝆖) should be interpreted in exactly the same way; nevertheless it is possible that  was intended.

III FINALE: Presto

A set of variations, though not so named. The structure is as follows:

Theme: bb.1–24 ‖: A (8 bars) :‖: BA (16 bars) :‖.
Var.1: 25–48 (occasional semiquavers are introduced).
Var.2: 49–72 (more continuous semiquaver movement).
Var.3: 73–104 (the repeat of A and the whole of BA are in the minor).
Var.4: 105–152 (in both A and BA the repeat is varied).

The sunny character of the *Theme* should be underlined by staccato quaver upbeats in both hands: 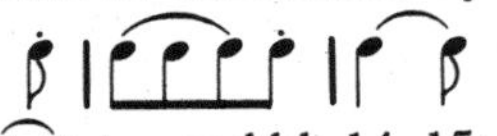 etc.; except in bb.5–6: 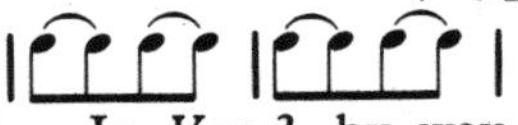 , and bb.14–15:  . In *Var.3*, by way of contrast, the sections in the minor are more reflective and *cantabile*.

3 SONATA in E flat, Hob.XVI/38

Sources used:

A 1st edition: No.4 of *Sei Sonate per il Clavicembalo, o Forte Piano . . . Opera XXX*; Artaria, Vienna [1780], Pl.No.7.

B *Oeuvres complettes*, Cahier II/4; Breitkopf & Härtel, Leipzig 1799–1806.

The present text is taken from A, but includes dynamics and additional phrase-marks from B.

I Allegro moderato

In keeping with the expansive character of the movement, the demisemiquavers throughout are *cantabile* rather than brilliant. In spite of the rests in bb.3–4 the opening sentence continues to the end of b.4; but the final quaver in bb.1 & 2 is an upbeat leading to the following bar. Note in b.13 how the 2nd-subject group begins with the opening of the 1st group transposed to the dominant – a device used by both Haydn and Mozart to combine unity with variety. In r.h. b.19 the initial gracenotes should anticipate the beat () in order to match the following figures. In b.21 a slight *rit.* is needed on the 2nd crotchet in preparation for the pause. The gracenotes are leisurely and melodic, the pause itself (on the E-flat) unhurried, and its resolution (on $\frac{\text{D}}{\text{B-flat}}$) *staccato* but without any trace of accent.

The surprising *p* on beat 1 of b.31 occurs in the source. If it is played it should be a *p subito*; but players might prefer to interpret it as  , like the editorial markings in bb.8, 29 & 57. In bb.35–39 the somewhat complicated fingering and distribution of notes between the hands has been suggested in order to achieve the necessary *legato*. These bars should be practised slowly, care being taken not to hold the isolated l.h. semiquavers for longer than their written value. In b.48 (a 'false recapitulation') the r.h. shake should probably be interpreted irregularly, as shown above the stave, otherwise the rhythm of the final six demisemiquavers will be obscured.

II Adagio

The ornamentation in r.h. b.3 shows that the quaver beat is very leisurely. In r.h. bb.1–2, etc., remember that Haydn's *staccato* dash (▾) means no more than a present-day *staccato* dot. Moreover, the sombre character of the movement suggests that it should be lightened still further to a *portato* (). It would be wise to moderate the *f* & *ff* in bb.10–11 (say to *mf* & *f* respectively), otherwise they are likely to sound out of scale with their surroundings. In b.19 it is easiest to think of the final beat as eight hemi-demisemiquavers with a pause on the initial E-flat; but the longer flourish in b.27 requires additional time. A slight *rit.* is implied before the pause in bb.42 & 45.

III FINALE: Allegro

As befits the forthright mood of this *tempo di menuetto*, the *staccatos* are shorter and more powerful than in the previous movement. In b.2 an editorial *staccato* dash has been added to the l.h. B-flat, not only because the source shows one in b.26, but also because a new *legato* phrase so obviously begins on beat 3. The r.h. at that point carries on with the pattern of 2-note slurs: 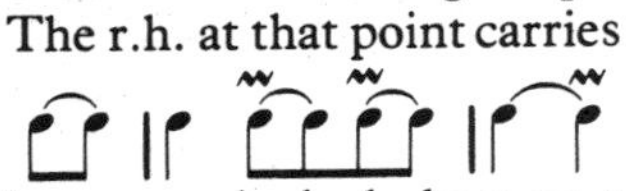 . This continues in the remaining unmarked r.h. bars up to b.28, with the exception of b.14 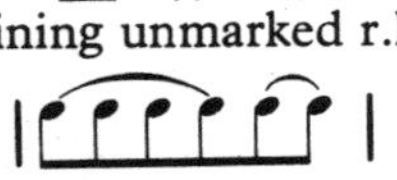 , b.19 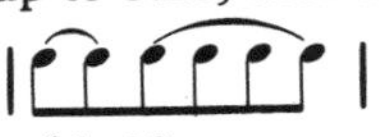 , and a *legato* from beat 3 of b.20 to the end of b.23.

In the central subdominant section – which is in fact the Trio of the Menuet – the r.h. *staccatos* are light, but still short. Bb.43–46 should be practised slowly (like bb.35–39 of the 1st movement) in order to achieve clear phrasing () in each part.

4 SONATA in A flat, Hob.XVI/43

Sources used:

- A An early copyist's MS titled *Sonata per Cembalo. Di Gius. Hayden.* (Berlin, Staatsbibliothek Preussischer Kulturbesitz, Mus.ms.10117.)
- B 1st edition: No.1 of *A Fifth Sett of Sonatas for the Piano Forte or Harpsichord*; Beardmore & Birchall, London 1783.

The present text follows A. Its 1st & 3rd movements (but not the 2nd) contain a number of dynamic marks shown as *pia*[*no*], *pianiss*[*imo*] and *for*[*te*].

I Moderato

Moderato here applies to minims, not crotchets (i.e. ¢, not C). In fact the crotchet beat is brisk enough to allow the quaver triplets to ripple along effortlessly, generally as a l.h. background, but at times (as in bb.37–46, etc.) assuming the principle role.

In bb.12 & 112 the first three gracenotes are short, since they occur on repeated notes (see the Introduction under *Ornamentation: Single small notes, 5*). But it is hard to decide whether the fourth should also be short (in order to continue the pattern), or long  (because it is *not* a repetition). Players should feel free to choose whichever version they prefer. Either way, beat 4 of b.14 should be interpreted as shown above the stave.

The l.h. *staccato* crotchets in bb.21–23, etc., are *non legato* rather than short, otherwise the mock-solemnity of the passage will be lost. At b.34 the surprise of the interrupted cadence can be heightened by fractionally delaying beat 1 and slightly lengthening the bar. (Strict *a tempo* on b.35.)

Towards the end of the development the 8-bar r.h. passage beginning at b.93 gradually acquires the feeling of a *quasi cadenza*. The quaint low E-flat in l.h. b.100 – which recalls the humour of the exposition's close (bb.54–55) – must be heard as the completion of the long r.h. shake: it should therefore follow the latter without any break.

II Menuetto

With the exception of bb.13–15, where the accent is on the 3rd beats, the most important note in the figure  is always the crotchet. It should be slightly accented and not too short. The crispness of the semiquaver, on the other hand, can very well be exaggerated. A *rit.* is needed in b.15 to prepare for the following pause – but note that the latter is on the rest and *not* on beat 1. In contrast to the perky 1st Menuet, the 2nd is *dolce cantabile* throughout. A little extra time can be taken over bb.33–34, in order to savour the expressive discord and its resolution.

III RONDO: Presto

The typically Haydnesque humour that has been lurking in the background of movements I & II here becomes explicit. It consists largely in doing what's unexpected. For example, the absurd l.h. E-flat quaver in b.18, which is all the more comic if the pause on the r.h. F is sustained until the sound has almost evaporated, and both r.h. and l.h. E-flats are held *pp* for no more than their written values.

The phrasing should be very pointed throughout; e.g. the opening thus:  , with paired quavers in b.7; bb. 42–45  ; and bb.46–56 *legatissimo* by way of contrast. The three l.h. notes in b.211 are a joke (*p staccatissimo*). Almost every reappearance of the opening theme contains small changes of detail, which must be underlined, *viz.* in r.h. bb.59, 65, 87, 131, 150, and specially the leaps in bb.194–200. Finally, in bb.225–228 a *pianissimo* ushers in unexpected quaver triplets, and the movement ends with a *forte* bump.

5 SONATA in E minor

This appears to be the original version of the Sonata in F, Hob.XVI/47, which was first published by Artaria in 1788 as *Oeuvre 55*. No autograph of either version has survived. As can be seen from the following table, each version contains a movement not included in the other:

E minor version		*F major version*
		I Moderato 3/4, F mi.
I Adagio 6/8, E mi.	=	II Larghetto 6/8, F mi.
II Allegro 2/4, E ma.	=	III Allegro 2/4, F ma.
III Tempo di Menuet 3/4, E ma.		

The E minor version is the only known source of its 3rd movement, the *Tempo di Menuet*. The opening *Moderato* of the F major version is so unlike Haydn that one wonders whether it is genuine. Possibly that version of the Sonata was put together by Artaria from two unrelated manuscripts.

Sources used:

- A E minor version: an early copyist's MS titled *Divertimento*, part of a volume containing works mainly by Haydn and titled *Divertimenta, ac Galantheriae Variae à Diversis Authoribus Conscriptae*. (Vienna, Gesellschaft der Musikfreunde, VII 40 623.)
- B F major version: *Oeuvres complettes*, Cahier IV/6; Breitkopf & Härtel, Leipzig 1799–1806.

The present edition follows A, but also makes use of some details from B.

I Adagio

In spite of the *fortes* in bb.2, 9, etc., the mood is predominantly lyrical, with a gently flowing quaver beat. The r.h. *legato* is only interrupted at such obvious points as the broadly detached quavers in b.9 and the appoggiaturas ( and ) in bb.13–15, etc. In b.11 the l.h. 10th can be avoided by substituting the equivalent bar from the F major version, as shown in footnote 2. The lovely interrupted cadence on beat 1 of b.46 initiates a questioning 2-bar bridge-passage that leads towards the next movement.

II Allegro

Bb.44–48 prove that this *Allegro* is considerably slower than its opening might suggest. Its almost bucolic good-humour is, in fact, sturdy rather than sparkling. All upbeat quavers are *staccato*. The awkward r.h. semiquavers in bb.36–37 & 125–126 require slow practice, with the wrist and forearm moving smoothly to the right as the passage ascends. In the development note that an unexpected 3-bar phrase begins with the upbeat to b.62.

III FINALE: Tempo di Menuet

Though this miniature sonata-form Finale looks perfectly straightforward, it is full of structural surprises. For example, in the 1st-subject group (bb.1–10) the second half of the opening 4-bar phrase is echoed (bb.5–6) before the entry of the answering 4 bars, thus increasing the paragraph from 8 bars to 10. The 2nd group (b.11*f*) begins with 4 + 3 bars, bb.2–3 of the latter being echoed and extended into a 4-bar phrase. The exposition then closes with 8 bars which surprisingly consist of 3 + 5.

The short development (bb.30–39) introduces new material (b.32*f*), which provides a reflective contrast (*sempre legato*) to the more extrovert feeling of the rest. Finally, in the recapitulation (b.40*f*) the 1st group is considerably expanded, in order to remain in the tonic key for the otherwise unaltered return of the 2nd group (b.54*f*).

Sonata in D

Hob.XVI/14

Before 1760

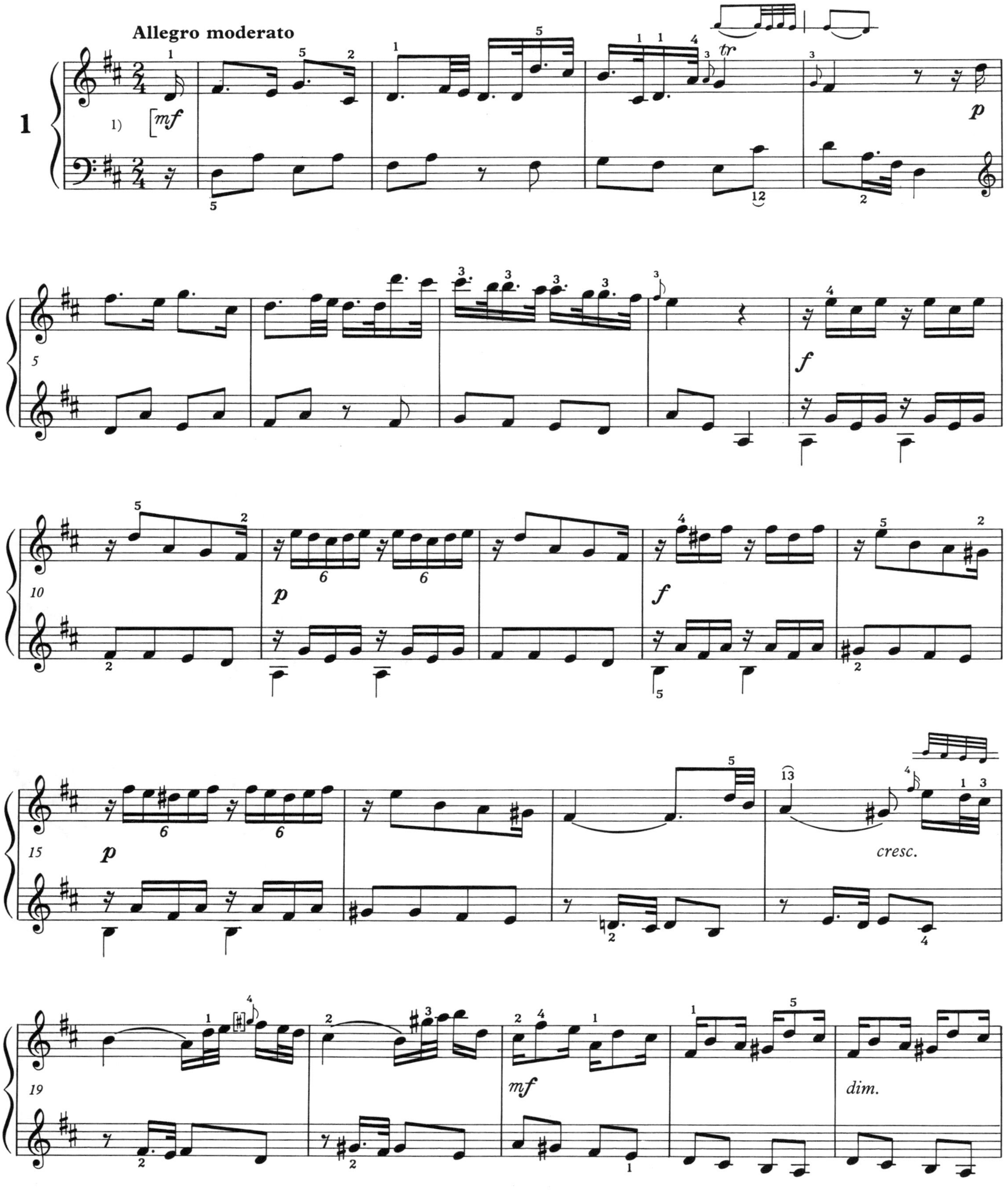
Allegro moderato
1
1)
mf
p
f
cresc.
dim.
tr

1) All dynamics in this Sonata are editorial, as there are none in the sources.

1) B.30, r.h. notes 1-2: both A & B have C-sharp C-natural; but the parallel passage, b.100, shows that both notes should be C-natural.

p
cresc.
f
tr
mf
p
cresc.
mf
dim.
p
mf
p

79
f
85
p
6
6
cresc.
90
f
dim.
p
95
f
p
100
cresc.
mf
105
p
tr
[♪ = c.120]

1) B.3, r.h. note 11: thus in B. A has G; but see b.17.
2) B.8, l.h. note 3: thus in B. A has an improbable C(sharp).

Menuet da Capo
[♩ = c.106]

3) B.33, r.h. note 3: thus in B. A has an improbable natural to the E; but see parallel passage, b.51.

Presto

1) B.41, r.h. note 1: A has gracenote B; but see more probable parallel passage, b.106. In B there is no gracenote in either bar.

2) B.63, r.h. note 2: thus in B. In A repeat dots are added to b.62, and b.63 is omitted.

3) B.78, r.h. upper line, notes 1-2: thus in B. A has two quavers.

Sonata in G

Hob.XVI/27

c.1776

1) All dynamics in this Sonata are editorial, as there are none in A.
2) B.22, r.h.: in A the ornament is on the B. B & C give the more probable version shown.

p
f
fp
cresc.
f
fp
cresc.
f
dim.
p

3) B.83, r.h. note 4: thus in C. A has G, which seems improbable; and B has F natural, which seems impossible.

118
123
p
f
128
fp
cresc.
f
133
fp
cresc.
f
138
dim.
p]
[♩ = c.88]

Menuet

18 *p*

22 *f*

26

31 *dim.* *p* *f*

35 *p*

Trio
p
mf
f
dim.
Menuet da Capo [♩ = c.112]

1) Bb. 4 & 20, l.h. note 2: A has a crotchet and no rest; but see the more probable bb.28, 44 & 76.

41

47 *f*

53 *f*

58 *p* *cresc.*

63 *mf* *f*

68

f
73
p
81
89
cresc.
mf
dim.
97
105
111

[♩ = c.120]

2) B.120, l.h. note 2: A has a crotchet and no rest.
3) B.143, r.h. notes 1-4: all the sources have GF(sharp)ED; but see the more probable b.127.

Sonata in E flat

Hob.XVI/38

Before 1780

1) Dynamics within square brackets or crossed with a small vertical stroke are editorial.

(a) Gracenotes as demi-semiquavers *before* the beat, here and in b.66, in order to match beats 1 & 2.

[mf
p
cresc.
f]
p [sub.]
f
[p
cresc.
mf
fp
cresc.
f
] p
cresc.
f
[p

(b) Exceptionally, the ornament anticipates the beat, to avoid rhythmic confusion.

[♪ = c.126]

(*a*) approximately

1) B.4: *pf* = *poco forte.*

(*b*) allow some extra time for this run.

2) B.20, r.h. beats 5 & 6: the natural & flat to the As are optional, as they only appear in B.

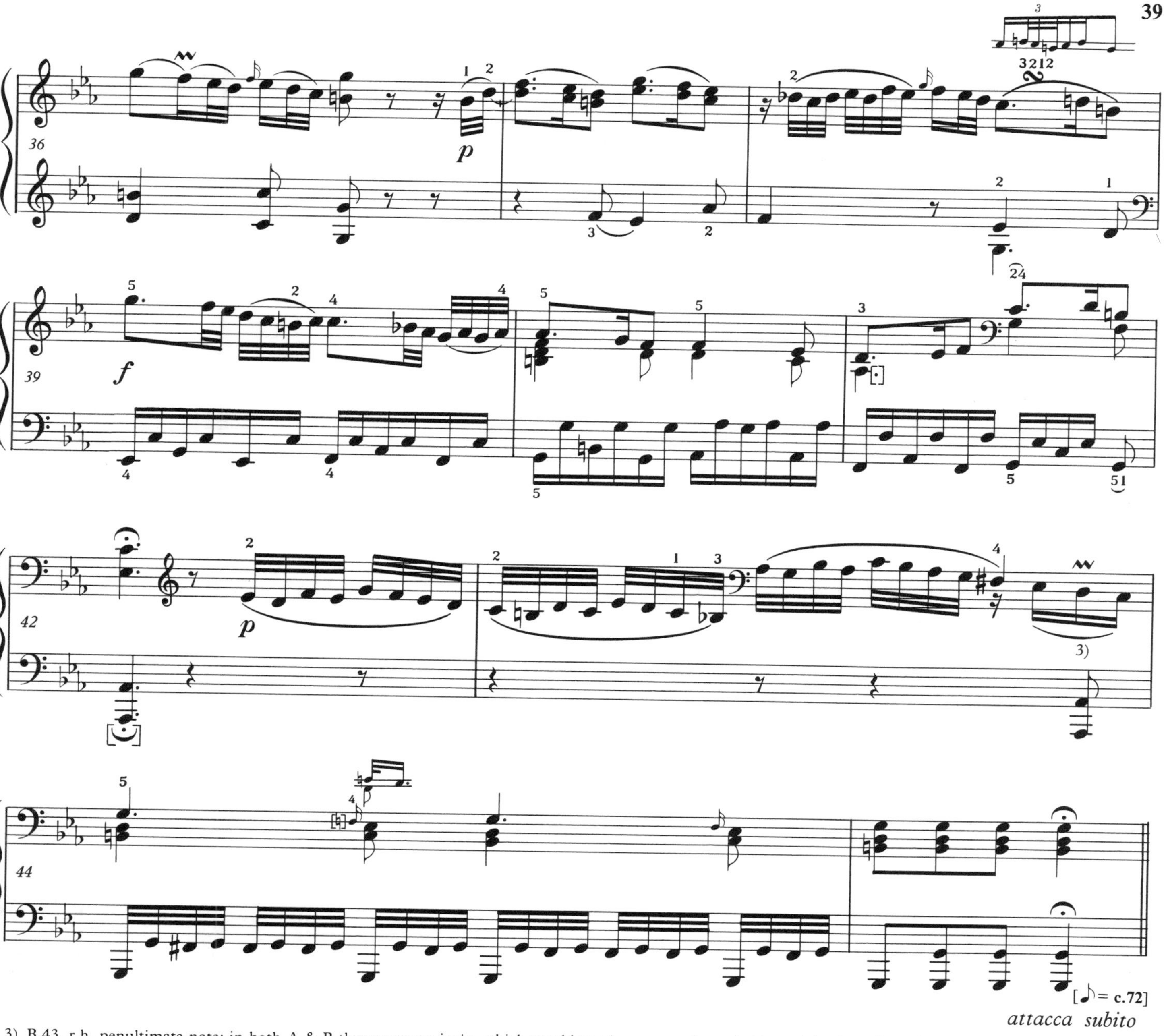
p
f
p
3)
[♪= c.72]
attacca subito

3) B.43, r.h. penultimate note: in both A & B the ornament is ⩫, which would produce a very improbable anticipation of the final C.

FINALE
Allegro
f
p
f

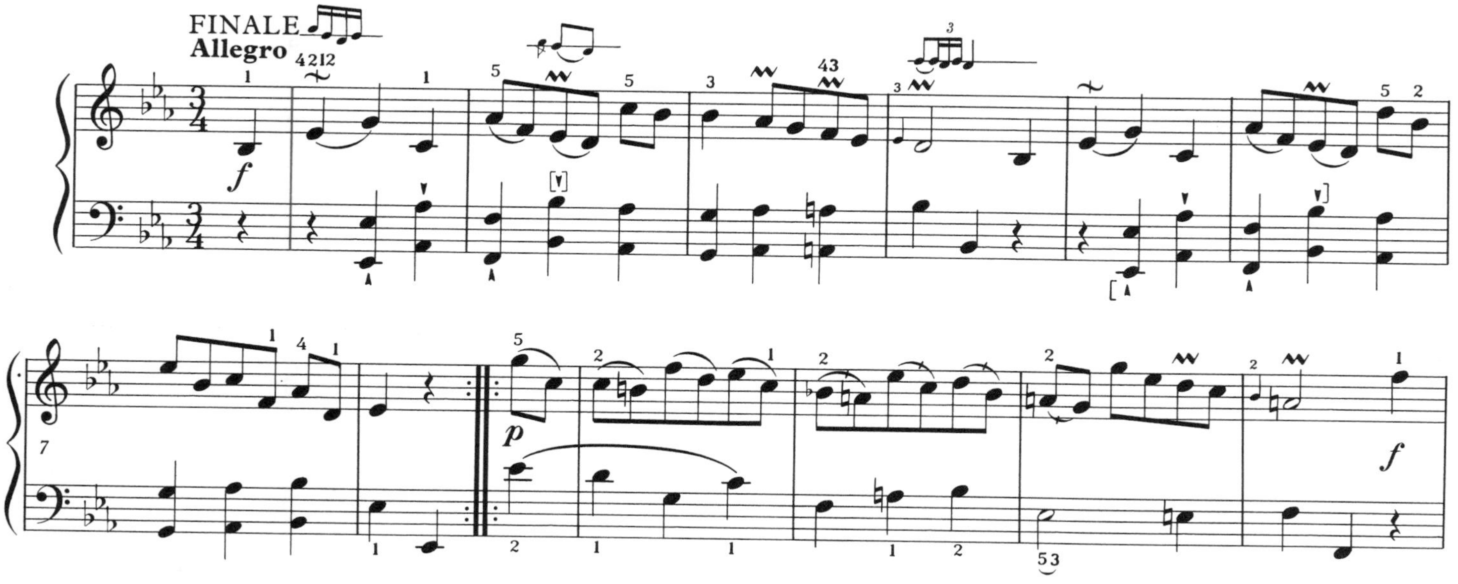

[Fine]
dolce
cresc.
mf
p
cresc.
mf
dim.
Da Capo
[♩ = c.126]

Sonata in A flat

Hob.XVI/43

Before 1783

1) All dynamics printed within square brackets are editorial. In movements I & III the comparatively few dynamics that appear in A are here shown as *forte*, *piano* & *pianissimo*.

2) B.24, l.h. final note: A (but not B) has D natural – an obvious slip.

3) B.32, l.h. note 7: no natural to B in A; but see b.125.

4) Bb.57 & 59, l.h. note 2: A has a crotchet; but see bb.2, 4, etc.

5) B.82, l.h. note 12: A (but not B) has F; probably a slip.
6) B.92, r.h. notes 3-5: A has a quaver & two semiquavers; but see previous bars, etc.

7) B.120, l.h. chord: a 3rd too high in A, but not in B.

129
[p sub.
cresc.
f
132
p
cresc.
f
135
ff]
138
tr
piano
tr
pianissimo
142
145
[♩ = c.126]

Menuetto
Menuetto 2do
Menuetto da Capo
[♩ = c.132]

RONDO
Presto

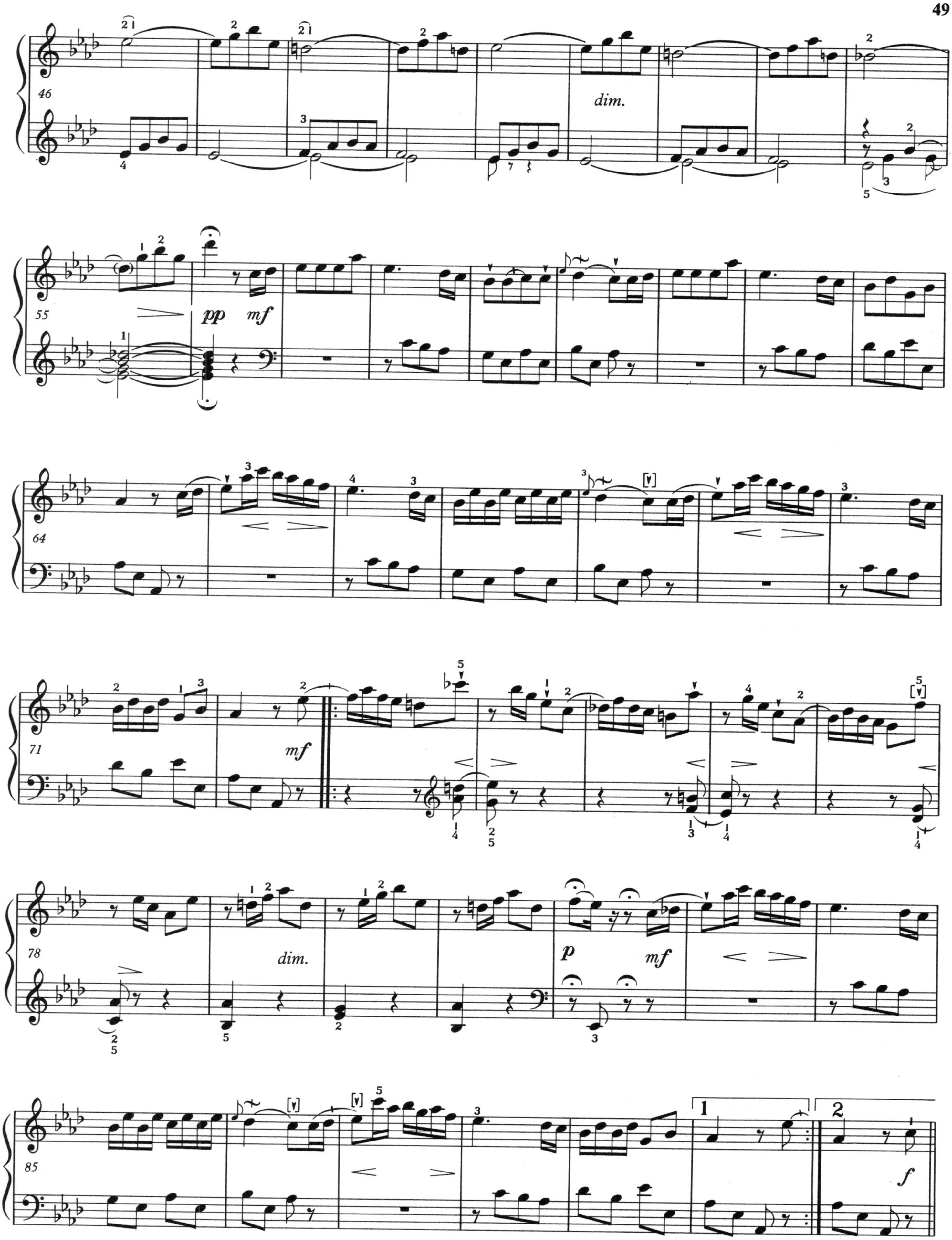
46
dim.
55
pp
mf
64
71
mf
78
dim.
p
mf
85
f

piano
forte

125
mf
132
mf
138
144
dim.
149
p
mf
156
1
2
f

162
p
167
f
172
dim. poco a poco
177
p
cresc. poco a poco
182
f
pp
188
mf

194

200

mf

207

dim.

Adagio

p

[Tempo primo]

213

mf

220

1

2

f

pianissimo

226

forte

[♩ = c.138]

Sonata in E minor

(Early version of Hob.XVI/47)

Before 1766

Adagio

5

1) There are no dynamics in A. Those given here in I & b.1 of II are from B; the remainder (shown within square brackets) are editorial.

2) B.11: B has the equivalent of   which players may prefer because of the absence of the l.h. 10th.

3) B.19, r.h. notes 2 & 3: A has D only. B gives the equivalent of the chord shown.

4) Bb.33-4 & 36, l.h.: A has the upper notes only of the octaves. B gives the versions shown.
5) B.45, r.h. notes 2-5: A has BAGF(sharp). B gives the more probable equivalent of BGF(sharp)E.
6) B.46, l.h. upper notes 2-4: A mistakenly has As.
7) B.47, l.h. note 1: A has only upper B quaver. B gives the dotted crotchet octave.

Segue Allegro
[♪ = c.104]

Allegro
f
p
cresc.

1) B.31, r.h. notes 4-5: A mistakenly duplicates b.32. B gives the correct reading.

56
p
cresc.
f
62
p
cresc.
67
f
p
73
f
p
pp
78
cresc.

2) Bb.100 & 103, r.h. note 4: both sources have F(sharp) or its equivalent; but see the more probable bb.11 & 14, which avoid hidden consecutive octaves.

3) B.136, l.h. 1st crotchet: A has ; but see the more probable b.47.

FINALE
Tempo di Menuet

1) B.8, l.h. note 1: A mistakenly has B.

2) B.32, r.h.: A mistakenly has five semiquavers.

Processed and printed by
Halstan & Co. Ltd., Amersham, Bucks., England